Sing for your Supper

NICK WARBURTON

Illustrated by Martin Cottam

Oxford University Press

Oxford University Press, Walton Street, Oxford OX2 6DP

Oxford New York
Athens Auckland Bangkok Bogota Bombay
Buenos Aires Calcutta Cape Town Dar es Salaam
Delhi Florence Hong Kong Istanbul Karachi
Kuala Lumpur Madras Madrid Melbourne
Mexico City Nairobi Paris Singapore
Taipei Tokyo Toronto

and associated companies in
Berlin Ibadan

Oxford is a trade mark of Oxford University Press

Printed in Great Britain

Illustrations by Martin Cottam

Photograph of Nick Warburton © Eaden Lilley Photography,
Cambridge

CHAPTER 1

Red Beard

The smell of mutton pies woke Jamie up.
His nose twitched before his eyes opened.

Jamie's mother was dead. His father
had gone to sea and not come back. He
remembered the big round sails as the
little galleon moved out of Plymouth
harbour, but he'd forgotten what his
father looked like. For two years he'd
lived on the streets and begged for his
food, so he got used to sniffing out pies.

He'd been dozing on a pile of straw
beside the horse trough when the man
walked by with his tray.

Pies, Jamie thought at once. Fat warm
pies.

He didn't have a coin to his name, but
he jumped up and followed the man. He
was heading for The Boar's Head.

Jamie saw him push his tray into the crowd at the door and disappear.

'After him,' Jamie said to himself.

He dropped to his knees and crawled through a forest of sturdy legs. Jamie could tell by a sniff that the pie man had stopped by a table in the corner. Keeping an eye open for the innkeeper, he crawled on. The pie man had set two steaming pies on the table. He was counting a handful of coins into his purse.

His customers weren't ordinary sailors. They wore stiff ruffs and a line of fancy buttons down the front of their tunics. Jamie had seen one of them around Plymouth before – the one with the red curly hair and the pointed beard.

He must be important, Jamie thought. Wherever he goes there's bustle and talk. But he looks like a man who might share his pie with a hungry boy.

'No mutton pies after we set sail,' the man with the red beard was saying to his friend. 'Ship's biscuits and hard cheese and not much else.'

'But maybe some Spanish gold to spend when we get back, eh, Francis?' his friend said.

Francis. So that was his name. And Spanish gold. That meant sea-fights, didn't it? Maybe they were pirates.

'Well, Master Francis,' Jamie said to himself, 'I can't wait for your gold but I'd like to share a bit of your pie.'

And he popped up from behind the table as the redheaded man was about to eat.

'Can I sing you a song, Master Francis?' Jamie asked him.

Francis blinked at him with his mouth still open.

'Please, Master,' Jamie said. 'A song for a mouthful of pie.'

The man laughed and asked him if he had a good voice.

'A wonderful voice, sir. Sweet as the birds, I promise.'

'If you want to earn the price of a pie,' said Francis's friend, 'you can go down to the harbour and help load our ship.'

'What ship is that, sir?' Jamie asked.

'The Pelican. And it's being loaded for a voyage to ...'

But before he could say another word, Francis held up a hand to stop him.

'Quiet, Will,' he said. 'A busy inn is not the place to talk about our plans.'

Will shut his mouth and looked round the noisy room. Jamie looked round, too. And sure enough – or so he thought – there was a thin man at the next table, leaning towards them as if to catch every word. For a second Jamie's eye met his, and the man scowled.

A face to sour the milk, Jamie thought. And full of trouble, too. After two years on the streets, Jamie knew trouble when he saw it.

A shiver of fear ran up his spine. But
Francis was speaking to him again.

'Come on then, lad,' he said. 'Sing up.'

Jamie opened his mouth to sing, but a broad hand took hold of his neck and he felt himself jerked to his feet.

'I've told you before,' boomed a voice. 'You leave my gentlemen in peace.'

It was the innkeeper. He crooked an arm round Jamie's throat and crushed him against his greasy apron.

Jamie kicked out and flailed his arms but it was no use. The innkeeper hauled him backwards to the door and swung him out into the night.

He twisted through the air and landed with a thud in the street. Instead of the smell of mutton, his nose was filled with the stench of straw and horse dung. It was the second time he had been thrown out of The Boar's Head that night.

He stood up and shook himself. Across the street he saw the glow of candle-light from The Swan. The hum of voices inside tempted him to try his luck there, but he'd been thrown out of The Swan, too. He didn't feel like being dumped in horse muck a fourth time.

'Oh well,' he mumbled as he wiped himself down, 'maybe I *should* go down to the harbour. If they're loading for a voyage, maybe I can pick up some scraps.'

Soon he heard the lap of water against wooden hulls and ropes slapping in the breeze. He saw masts swaying against the blue-black sky. The ship in front of him was *The Pelican*. There were others, too, lined up behind it.

The harbour was busy for the time of night. Dark figures with sacks on their shoulders hurried backwards and forwards. Some dumped their loads on the harbour wall and others tottered up planks onto the ships.

He stopped one of the sailors and asked if he could help.

'Clear off, little 'un,' the sailor growled. 'You'll only get under our feet.'

Jamie sighed and sat down in the shadow of a wall. His stomach grumbled with hunger in the dark. His head hurt. He watched the men loading their stores. He'd seen ships being loaded many times. Once he'd seen a sack drop and split open, sending cheeses rolling over the cobbles.

A good round cheese would do nicely now, he thought. Maybe someone'll drop a few sacks tonight. Sack after sack he saw carried onto the ships. But no one stumbled. Nothing spilled. At last the men stopped work and went off together, laughing and joking.

For a while Jamie watched the moon climb slowly in the sky. Then he stood up and stretched.

'Nothing doing here,' he said softly to himself.

He was about to wander back into Plymouth Town when something caught his eye.

Two of the men came back. Or were they the same men? It was too dark to see properly and they were wrapped in long cloaks.

They moved like the men who'd loaded the ships, trotting along with their heads bowed, but there was something different about them.

At first Jamie couldn't think what it was. Then it came to him. They had no sacks on their backs. They were running up the plank onto *The Pelican* but they carried no stores. He saw them drop into the ship and disappear in shadow. Jamie sat down again and waited.

A man with a lantern on a pole came wandering along – the watchman, keeping his eye on the ships with their load of fresh stores. He walked steadily along the harbour wall until he reached the ship furthest from *The Pelican*. Then he paused for a moment before turning round. It was then that the two men came scuttling down the plank again.

One was tall with pale hands which fluttered in the dark. Jamie knew him. It was the sour-faced man from The Boar's Head. The other man was short and thick-set.

They moved nimbly and silently, and
this time they were carrying something.
At least, the short one was. It was more
like a black bag than a sack and the short
man carried it on his shoulder like a barrel.

Jamie shrank back into the shadow of a
wall. He saw the men look round and spot
the watchman. The tall man stooped and
picked up a stone in his pale hands.

He hurled it high over the masts of *The Pelican* and Jamie heard it drop into the sea with a deep splash.

Along the harbour wall the watchman heard it too. He spun round and held himself still. Then he lifted his lantern and peered between the ships, trying to see where the sound had come from.

While he was still staring at the sea, the men hurried away in the opposite direction, their cloaks flapping behind them as they ran.

CHAPTER 2

Pale hands

Jamie's mind was racing. He knew that something odd was going on. He waited until the men were almost out of sight, then set off after them. When they turned into a side street, he forced himself to run faster.

Mustn't lose them now, he thought as he pounded along. They'll disappear down some dark alley. I must keep up.

Jamie had seen plenty of thieves on the streets, but these two were different – and he was sure they were dangerous. Common sense told him to stay out of it. But he was curious. And maybe there was the chance of pleasing Red Beard and earning some pie. Maybe even something better than pie.

'Mustn't lose them,' he said to himself over and over. 'Mustn't lose them.'

As soon as the men reached the safety of a side street, they stopped running to catch their breath.

They were bending down to examine the thing in the black bag, when Jamie hurtled round the corner and ran straight into them.

He fell over one and rolled onto the other. There were rough shouts, the rustle of cloaks and a waving of arms.

Jamie's struggle didn't last long.

Soon he felt a knee on his chest and long fingers tightening on his arm. He twisted his head and saw the same pale hand that had thrown the stone. There was a silver ring on the middle finger. A face came close and spoke to him in a harsh voice.

'And where do you think you're going?'

It was the broad man, the one who was kneeling on him, and the stench of his breath made Jamie flinch.

'I'm sorry, master,' he said. 'I'm sorry.'

Then the tall man spoke and his voice was a thin whisper.

'He's following us, Tom. I saw him talking to Red Beard in The Boar's Head.'

'No, sir,' said Jamie. 'I'm not following you, I'm running away, sir. Honest. The watchman's after me.'

The fingers loosened on Jamie's arm and the men darted a look at each other. They glanced nervously back at the corner of the street.

They only looked away for a second but it was enough for Jamie. He wriggled from under Tom's knee and scrambled to his feet.

The men grabbed at him, missed, and he was charging off into the darkness.

'Hey! Come back here!' the man called
Tom shouted after him.

Jamie dived into an alley and barked
his shin against something he couldn't
see. From the way it clattered against
the wall behind him he guessed it was
an empty barrel. The men came
lumbering after him and one of them
kicked the barrel too.

Jamie came to a gap between two
houses and ran blindly into it, hoping
there'd be nothing in his way this time.
There wasn't.

He groped along a wall until he found
a low fence. He swung himself over it
and dropped into a little garden.

His fingers touched damp cabbage leaves and a fish head. He crouched there wide-eyed, trying to still his gasping breath.

Heavy feet thudded by him, only yards away. The sound disappeared into the night and then there was silence. He waited. A dog barked in the distance. A sharp pain began to throb in his leg. He hadn't noticed it when he was running.

After two or three more minutes he let out a long sigh and climbed painfully out of the garden.

'You should save your nose for sniffing out pies, Jamie,' he told himself. 'And keep it clear of bad men in long cloaks.'

He imagined what the men might do if they caught him. The thought made him shudder.

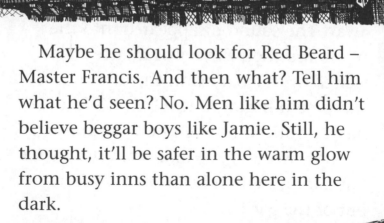

Maybe he should look for Red Beard – Master Francis. And then what? Tell him what he'd seen? No. Men like him didn't believe beggar boys like Jamie. Still, he thought, it'll be safer in the warm glow from busy inns than alone here in the dark.

So he rubbed his leg and started slowly through back streets and alleyways towards the heart of the town. After a while he found himself outside The Boar's Head again.

'Well, here I am again,' Jamie said out loud, 'and I'm worse off than I was before. Still, I'll be safe and warm in here, as long as I keep my head down.'

He slid in at the door and looked cautiously around.

The place was full, and noisy with talk
and laughter. The pie seller had gone but
he thought he might be able to scrounge
a scrap of bread. He squeezed onto the
nearest bench and made himself as small
as he could.

The men next to him kept their backs
turned and talked in low voices. Jamie
could see two beakers of ale on the table
in front of them. There was no bread,
though, so he soon lost interest in them.

He was looking round for more
promising customers when one of the
men reached out to pick up his beaker.

Jamie turned and looked, then looked
again and his heart gave a sudden jump.

The man's hand was long and pale,
with a silver ring on the middle finger.

CHAPTER 3

A bit of bread and cheese

'I told you, Tom,' Jamie heard the thin man say. 'The boy was in here talking to Red Beard. He was watching *The Pelican*. He must be a spy.'

'What if he is?' Tom said shortly. 'We've got what we were after, Jack. And if we see him again I'll do for him. No need to worry then.'

'If, Tom. If we see him again.'

'Stop going on about it. A scrap of a kid like that can't harm us.'

The man called Jack sighed and shook his head. He banged the beaker down on the table so hard it made Jamie jump.

They'll kill me, Jamie thought. And nobody will know or care. I've got to get away from here.

He glanced quickly at the open door. There were three or four people standing by it, laughing away as if they didn't have a care in the world.

Just then Tom coughed and leaned over to spit on the floor. Jamie caught a glimpse of his broad face and his heart began to pound in his chest.

Run, he thought. Run, Jamie, and run now.

But as he turned away, a huge sailor with a thick brass ring through his ear plomped down beside him.

And he was trapped, squashed
between the sailor and thin-faced Jack.

His head began to spin and points of
candle-light swum before his eyes. And
Jack had seen him. Jamie saw his mouth
drop open – a gaping red mouth studded
with two or three black teeth.

'You,' the mouth said in a whispery
voice.

The hand with the ring took Jamie by the shoulder and squeezed. Jamie squirmed but could not break free.

His face was white with fear. The big sailor nudged him fiercely and told him to sit still.

'Look what we've got here, Tom,' hissed Jack.

Tom blinked with shock at the sight of Jamie sitting there. Then he scowled, drew a fat finger across his throat and gave a silent laugh. That awful gesture terrified Jamie. He opened his mouth and a thin, squeaking sound came out.

'Shut up,' snapped Jack and shook his shoulder.

The sailor turned to look at Jamie.

'What's up with him?' he asked.

'Nothing,' said Jack with a sickly smile. 'He's just singing a little song, aren't you, lad?'

Jamie nodded. Just singing. Singing for his supper. He took a breath and began to sing in a wavery voice. He couldn't think of a tune so he made one up.

'A bit of b-b-bread and cheese is all I ask,' he sang. 'All I ask is a bit of b-b-bread and cheese.'

'That'll do,' Jack hissed into his face.

'Take him outside,' growled Tom. 'Quick!'

I'm done for, Jamie thought. I'm done for now.

But he went on singing. Then he saw the innkeeper pushing his way through the crowd towards them.

'You again!' he bellowed. 'How many times do I have to tell you?'

He reached across the table and grabbed Jamie by the front of his tunic. People looked round and cheered as the innkeeper lifted him off the bench and swung him into the air.

'Let him be!' laughed the sailor. 'He only wants to sing.'

The innkeeper dropped Jamie and he clattered to the floor and crawled under the table. He felt his head bump into something hard and black. At first he thought it was someone's knee, but it made a hollow sound against his head, not at all like a knee. Then Tom's head appeared beneath the table. He snarled and lunged at Jamie. Jamie lurched backwards. Someone caught hold of his ankles and he felt himself being dragged belly-down across the floor.

It's Jack, he thought. He's got me!
But it wasn't Jack. It was the innkeeper,
and he was marching Jamie to the door.

Everyone shouted and cheered as he swung his leg and kicked Jamie into the street.

Jamie skidded and rolled over, then jumped up and ran. He ran until he reached the corner of the street. When he looked back, he saw Tom and Jack, stuck in the doorway of The Boar's Head, trying to shove their way out. Their faces were twisted with rage.

'Go, Jamie,' he told himself. 'Run, run, run!'

But his legs were weak with fright and running wasn't easy. He looked down and found that he was still clutching the black thing he'd found under the table.

He peered down at it and froze in his tracks.

'Stone the crows,' he said to himself. 'Not that.'

Then he took off.

CHAPTER 4

Out of the black bag

Jamie swung the bundle over his shoulder and bolted. As he ran he could hear a hollow sound thumping against his back. And something rattling too.

What could it be? What kind of treasure rattled like that?

He heard Tom and Jack roaring up and down the streets behind him. This time, though, he had a good start.

Five minutes later, after twisting and turning down narrow lanes, he lost them completely. At last he came to a church yard and slipped in among the graves. He found a shadowy spot behind a tall headstone and fell to his knees to rest.

The night was now thick and dark but a little light filtered down from a small moon. He set the bag down and examined it.

It was tied at the top with a piece of white cord. His fingers fiddled nervously at the knot and he pulled the black cloth away. A pale disc appeared. He touched it gently. It felt like paper or tight leather, and it made a soft booming sound.

A drum.

Jamie was disappointed. A drum. And
a couple of dull sticks. They must have
made the rattling sound. All that fuss
for an old drum! He kicked it away in
disgust.

'I thought you'd be treasure,' he told
it. 'I thought you'd be important. A
stupid old drum! What use is that?'

He turned his back on it and folded his arms. Then he took the black cloth bag and wrapped it round him. He leaned against the headstone and closed his eyes.

'This is more use than a stupid old drum,' he grumbled. 'At least this'll keep me warm.'

He yawned and thought about his night's work: all that flying through the air and landing in horse muck, all that running away from men in cloaks. What was it for, and where had it got him? Alone in a graveyard with a worthless drum. A worthless drum in a lonely graveyard. The words tumbled over and over in his head, and a minute or two later he was fast asleep.

Spots of cold rain on his face and a pattering sound woke him up. There was a stiff pain in his neck as he sat up. He blinked in the morning light. The drum was still where he'd kicked it. Raindrops were bouncing off it.

'You're no use to me,' he scowled at it. He sat there staring at it and thinking. What was he going to do with it?

He could smash it up and make a little fire with it: it might warm him for ten minutes or so. Or he could take it to the market and try to sell it. But if he took it to the market, he might end up being chased through every street in Plymouth again.

'Useless thing,' he muttered.

But it looked a little more grand in daylight. It was not an ordinary drum. It was well made and brightly painted with little pictures. After all, Tom and Jack had stolen it from *The Pelican*, and they must've thought it was worth something.

I'll have to take it back, he thought. *Someone* will be pleased to see it. Of course, Tom and Jack might catch me with it, but that's a risk I'll have to take.

He got up and stretched and shivered.

'That's what I'll do, then,' he said to himself. 'I'll take it back.'

CHAPTER 5

A good turn

The harbour was again bustling with activity when he arrived. The last of the stores were being loaded. One or two richly-dressed men were pacing about, calling instructions to sailors who trotted up gangplanks with sacks and barrels.

'These barrels of tar for *The Pelican*!' someone shouted. 'And candles! More candles and cloth aboard *The Marigold*! Move yourselves, move yourselves!'

Jamie watched as men clung to masts
and spars, tightening ropes and checking
sails. Gulls circled and screamed above.

After a while Jamie stopped in front of a short fat sailor with his head bent forward under a heavy sack.

'Please, master,' he began, but the sailor only growled at him.

He squinted at Jamie, swayed under his load, then took a step or two backwards and aimed a kick at him.

'Out of my way, you brat! Can't you see we're busy?'

'Pig!' Jamie called after him as he jumped nimbly aside.

No use asking the men with stores to carry, he realized; better to ask someone coming off the ships empty-handed.

'Excuse me, master, but I've got something here ...'

But the empty-handed sailors didn't want to know either. And they had their hands free to take a swipe at anyone who dared to get in their way.

And the fine gentlemen shouting out
their orders only wrinkled their noses at
him and flapped him out of the way.

'Out of the way, boy! Out of the way!'

'Don't any of you want to see what
I've got here?' Jamie shouted at them.

But nobody did. They bustled about, running and carrying and shouting, and they took no notice of him. He sighed heavily and sat on a low wall with the drum on his lap.

What could he do with it now? He couldn't sell it in the market and he couldn't give it back. And what would they want with a drum on a long voyage anyway? They'd need tar and candles, beef and pork, biscuits and cloth – but a drum? Even a fancy drum like this one was no use to anyone.

He folded back the cloth and looked at the drum. One of the sticks dropped at his feet and he picked it up. He tapped it lightly against the tight skin. It made a deep, pleasing sound. He found the other stick and gave the drum a couple of rattling blows.
Yes, he liked the noise it made.

He tapped sharply with the sticks, trying to beat a rhythm like the men who played for the dancing bears.

A rat-a-tat-tat BONG BONG!

A rat-a-tat-tat BONG BONG!

When he stopped, the drum echoed into silence. In fact, the whole harbour seemed to be quiet now. The shouting had stopped and he couldn't hear the pounding of feet on planks any more. He looked up.

The sailors and the men in their rich clothes were standing still and staring at him. Then one or two began to move. They walked slowly towards him. Jamie gazed from face to face and swallowed. Soon he seemed to be surrounded by hundreds of men, all of them looking at him, all of them waiting.

'What?' he said quietly. 'What is it?'

Someone was pushing his way through the crowd. A short man with curly red hair. The others moved aside to let him pass. He stopped in front of Jamie and frowned down at him.

And Jamie knew him. It was Master Francis. Red Beard.

'What have you got there, young man?' he asked quietly.

'It's a drum,' Jamie stammered. 'It was stolen from *The Pelican* and I've brought it back.'

'Did you steal it?'

'No, master. I saw two men run off with it. A thin man named Jack and an ugly one called Tom, and I got it away from them and I've brought it back and ... and ...'

'And you've done me a good turn,' said Francis. 'In fact, you've done your country a good turn. Those men were enemies of Queen Elizabeth. Spies, working for Spain. They'd do anything to stop me setting out in *The Pelican*.'

'But, master,' Jamie said, 'it's only an old drum ...'

'No, no, lad. It's my drum. It's Drake's drum, and it brings me luck. I can't set sail without it.'

Drake! Drake's drum. Jamie caught his breath. Of course. Francis. Red Beard. Why didn't he think of it before? Everyone in Plymouth knew about Francis Drake.

'Drake's drum is more than just a drum,' Francis was saying. 'When my men hear the beat of my drum they know I'm near and they rally round. That drum is the hope of England.'

The hope of England! And Jamie had nearly used it for firewood!

'What's your name, lad?'

'Jamie.'

'And what work do you do, Jamie?'

'No work, sir. I have to beg for my food.'

Francis Drake turned to one of the men and waved his hand.

'Take the drum to my cabin. And bring young Jamie too. He's a good brave lad; just the sort to be my cabin boy.'

And suddenly everyone started talking and laughing at once, and Jamie was being led towards *The Pelican*. Hands reached out to ruffle his hair and slap him on the back.

A good brave lad, he thought as he was jostled along. Me. Jamie. I've done a good turn for my country, and there's better work for me than begging. Cabin boy on *The Pelican*. A share in Spanish gold. And then ...

Mutton pies, he thought. As many mutton pies as I can eat.

NOTE:

Francis Drake set sail from Plymouth in *The Pelican* – later renamed *The Golden Hind* – on 15th November 1577. He led a small fleet which included *The Elizabeth*, *The Marigold*, *The Swan*, and *The Benedict*. Drake was said to have loved music, and some say he took with him a drum which he used to rally his men to him.

Few people knew his destination when he set out, but by the time he returned, nearly four years later, he had sailed round the world, the first Englishman to do so.

The men who returned with him – including the cabin boy – were made rich by the voyage.

About the author

I live in Cambridge but I was born in Essex and I still follow the fortunes of Essex County Cricket Club with great interest.

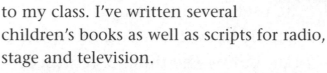

Before becoming a writer, I was a teacher for ten years and enjoyed best of all reading stories to my class. I've written several children's books as well as scripts for radio, stage and television.

I think Francis Drake must have been a fascinating character. I still remember a poem called Drake's Drum which I learned when I was about ten.

Other books at Stages 12, 13, and 14 include:

Billy's Luck by Paul Shipton
Cool Clive by Michaela Morgan
Call 999! by Sylvia Moody
Front Page Story by Roger Stevens
Pet Squad by Paul Shipton

Also available in packs
Stages 12/13/14 pack   0 19 916879 2
Stages 12/13/14 class pack   0 19 916880 6